W9-DEU-320

our
generation®

This is Layla's story.

LAYLA™

A SONG FROM MY HEART

BY

SUSAN CAPPADONIA LOVE

ILLUSTRATED BY TRISH ROUELLE

An Our Generation® *book*

MAISON JOSEPH BATTAT LTD. *Publisher*

A very special thanks to the editor,
Joanne Burke Casey.

Our Generation® Books is a registered trademark of Maison Joseph Battat Ltd.
Text copyright © 2014 by Susan Love
Characters portrayed in this book are fictitious. Any references to historical
events, real people, or real locales are used fictitiously. Other names,
characters, places, and incidents are products of the author's imagination,
and any resemblance to actual events or locales or persons, living or dead,
is entirely coincidental.
All rights reserved, including the right of reproduction in whole or in part
in any form.
ISBN: 978-0-9891839-6-3
Printed in China

*For Don McCasland and
all the folks who make the
Blue Hill Observatory
a very special place*

Read all the adventures in the
Our Generation® Book Series

Read more about **Our Generation®** books and dolls online:
www.ogdolls.com

CONTENTS

EXTRA! EXTRA! READ ALL ABOUT IT!
*Big words, wacky words, powerful words, funny words…
what do they all mean? They are marked with this symbol *.
Look them up in the Glossary at the end of this book.*

Chapter One

THE BIG BREAK

"Wah-HOOOOOOO!" I yelled, pumping my fists in the air.

It was the moment I'd been dreaming about, but never really thought would happen. And then it actually did, while I was cruising along in my tour bus, somewhere between Dallas, Texas and Santa Fe, New Mexico.

I grabbed the phone that I'd accidentally dropped and gripped it tightly beside my ear.

"Are you still there, Donna?" I asked. Donna is my manager, the person who schedules me to sing and play guitar in concerts.

"I sure am, kiddo," Donna boomed over the phone. "This is your big break*, Layla! Your once-in-a-lifetime chance to be a star!"

"Please tell me all about it again," I

9

begged her, "and start from the beginning!"

"It would be my pleasure," she replied happily. I could tell that she was as excited as I was. "The Brisbee Brothers Band wants you to perform at their Five Star Concert."

Wow! I thought. *I've admired the Brisbee brothers since before I started playing the guitar.*

Donna explained the deal once more: I'd be the warm-up act that would entertain* the audience before the five Brisbee brothers went onstage. She said the concert was so hot that tickets had sold out in nine minutes. I'd be playing in front of thousands of people.

"Girls your age hardly ever get to perform with musicians this famous," Donna said.

"Why did they pick me?" I asked.

"Because you're a special kid and a talented musician," Donna told me. "I'm not the only one who thinks so, either. Let me read what a music reviewer wrote about you in today's newspaper."

Young Star
Knows How to Shine

Layla's performance last night proves once again that she is the musician to watch. This girl knows how to sing! And play the guitar and write her own songs and charm the crowd, too.

Kids love Layla because she performs her own original* songs. Parents love Layla because her lyrics* send good messages about friendship, family and kindness. And just about everybody loves Layla because her catchy music makes you happy.

Plus, Layla has a colorful personality from head-to-toe, with her glittering blue star-shaped sunglasses, lilac sneakers and bright blue guitar. If you missed her act last night, you have one more chance to see her perform while she's in town. Tonight only, at the Grand Theater, 6:30 p.m.

Oh my goodness! I thought. *Really?!*

Donna added, "There's another reason why the band chose you. Remember when you went to their concert last year?"

"Yes!" I hooted. "It was pure luck that I got to go backstage and meet them. When I told them I was a songwriter, the Brisbee brothers

11

even let me play one of my songs for them."

"It was more than just luck, Layla. It was smart of you to bring your guitar," Donna told me. "They remembered that song all this time. Now, how about if you put your mom on the phone so I can spread the good news?"

"She's driving the tour bus right now," I said. "Can she call you back when we stop to eat lunch?"

"Sure thing, Layla," Donna said. "We'll work out the details then."

As soon as we said goodbye and hung up, I did a little dance in my seat and yelled, "I'm going to play with the Brisbee Brothers Band!"

My mom and Auntie both squealed with delight. Auntie is my Aunt Marie, who travels with us and takes turns driving the tour bus with my mom. Sometimes my dad takes a few days off from work to be with us, too.

"Did you know that after each Brisbee Brothers Band concert the whole crew who works on it gets together for a huge ice cream party?" I asked. "As much ice cream as you want, any flavors, toppings, cones, banana splits, sundaes, you name it."

I imagined eating Superduperscooper Strawberry Swirl with bananas, chocolate sauce and sprinkles. I could almost taste it already!

I couldn't wait to tell Olivia about the Five Star Concert. Olivia is my best friend and

she lives in our hometown, Majestic Mountain. She's not only the nicest person I know, she's probably my biggest fan, too. She even started the Layla Fan Club at our school.

Maybe Olivia can come with me to the concert, I thought.

The day before, Olivia had called to tell me that she and a few of our friends made posters with my photo on them. The posters advertised the Majestic Fest, a big festival* that's held annually* on the mountain where we live.

Something that makes our mountain special is that there is a weather observatory at the very top where weather is studied. The view of nature is amazing!

During the festival, there are tons of fun things to do at the observatory, plus activities on the trails, and a stage at the bottom of the mountain where musical performances take place.

The festival is where I learned how to

make a tornado in a bottle, found out what weather is like on other planets, flew a kite that does all kinds of tricks in the air, met a female meteorologist* and watched a lightning demonstration*.

Last year I'd made a promise to my town that I would perform at the Majestic Fest this year and write a new song especially for it. I wanted to give something back to the people in my town who had all given so much support to me.

I reminded myself that I had to get going writing that song. *But right now I'm going to think about how delicious the Superduperscooper Strawberry Swirl ice cream with bananas, chocolate sauce and sprinkles will be.*

As we traveled across the miles to my next performance, I wore my pink DJ headphones with the stars on them and began singing along to a song on my MP3 player. That's what I always do when I'm happy or want to get happy fast.

And I'd been *very* happy lately, traveling to small concerts as the warm-up act. So far I'd played in 18 different states and 47 cities!

Of course, all this touring took me far away from my hometown. Majestic Mountain is thought by many (including me) to have one of the most spectacular views on the planet.

After taking only a few quick trips back home during the past year, I missed sitting on my back porch. We live halfway up the mountain. From our porch I can see the green valley, winding river and colorful buildings and rooftops clustered around our small town.

I also missed hiking up to the weather observatory and getting a whiff of the pink roses that grow wild and smell like perfume.

But you can't be in two places at once, and I was lucky to be on the road. Writing songs, making music and performing is who I am and what I love. Yes, I felt very happy and very lucky…until one hour and twenty-eight minutes later.

Chapter Two

A HARD CHOICE

One hour and twenty-one minutes later we parked the tour bus at a rest stop along the highway. Auntie was slicing a watermelon and I was adding shredded carrots and pickles to roll-up sandwiches in the kitchenette* of the tour bus.

While we are on the road, the bus is our traveling home. It even has flip-down bunk beds and a tiny bathroom with a shower.

My mom sat at the kitchenette table and called Donna back. She was all smiles and nodding her head as she listened to the good news about the concert. Then suddenly her face became serious.

"Are you sure about that?" my mom asked Donna. She frowned deeply and told

Donna she'd have to talk with me. She'd call her back later.

Scooting over to the table, I sat down across from my mom.

"What's wrong, Mom?" I asked.

"Layla," my mom said gently, "about the Brisbee Brothers Band concert...."

I was sure that I knew what she was about to say. "Mom, I know I haven't played at a concert that big—but don't worry—I'm not nervous. Really."

"No, honey, it's not that." She bit her lip lightly. "The Five Star Concert...it's the same day as the Majestic Fest."

The problem became crystal clear: the Promise. The Promise that I'd made to play at the festival. But that was almost a whole year ago...*a lot* had happened since then.

A lot had happened that day. I was on my way to becoming a celebrity*.

I had a solution. "Maybe I could perform at the festival in the afternoon and then perform at the concert that night."

"I wish it could be that easy," my mom said. "There are just two hours between the start times of each event and they take place hundreds of miles apart. It's not possible."

"Oh nooooooo," I groaned.

"This is a hard one, Layla," my mom

said with a sigh. "Give it some thought. I know you'll make a good choice."

There IS no good choice, I thought. *How could I decide between accepting a chance to become a famous musician and keeping a promise I'd made to my whole town?*

I put my headphones back on, hoping the music would swirl around me and wrap me up in happiness.

As the tour bus motored* down the road, over bridges, across farmland, around lakes and through towns, my mind raced. I was determined to find a way to get out of playing at the festival.

When I started out in music, I played anywhere I could—at the park, libraries, birthday parties and the local art center. Then I began getting paid to play for bigger parties and events.

I had put my whole heart into practicing and traveling from city to city. What I enjoy most about being a musician is that it makes

21

people feel good inside.

It's been a lot of fun (and a lot of hard work, too) and I wasn't going to pass up this chance to play in front of thousands of people.

Nope! I thought. *I might never get asked to do a concert this amazing again.*

An idea popped into my head. *What if I promised to perform at the Majestic Fest next year instead of this year? Perfect plan! I'll tell Olivia. Surely everyone in Majestic Mountain would understand.*

Phew! That settled it. I leaned back into the tour bus seat, relaxed and drifted off to sleep.

I dreamt that I was in a giant pumpkin patch looking for a "just perfect" pumpkin to carve into a jack-o'-lantern. What seemed like thousands of big, round, orange pumpkins on vines covered the huge field.

Along came a farmer who told me that all the pumpkins had been sold except two.

"Your choice," the farmer told me,

pointing to a lonely pair of pumpkins sitting on a long wooden bench.

One of the pumpkins was very tall and skinny. It leaned so far to the left, it seemed as if it was about to fall over. The other one had no stem and was completely straight on the bottom. It reminded me of a flat tire.

In my dream, I thought, *there IS no good choice.* A mosquito kept buzzing around me— *Zzzzzzzz! Zzzzzzzz!* I felt very annoyed*. *Zzzzzzzz!*

Now half awake, I realized the sound wasn't a mosquito and it wasn't in my dream. I'd fallen asleep with the phone in my hand and it was vibrating*. My eyelids fluttered open and I saw that the phone was lit up.

I pressed the "on" button. "Hello?" I said drowsily.

"Hey! It's me, your best friend the weather geek," Olivia said. "I'm calling from the weather observatory. Guess how many tickets to the Majestic Fest have been sold already? Guess!

Two hundred and three! You're the biggest star the festival has seen in years!"

When Olivia gets excited, she talks nonstop. "If the festival earns enough money to keep the observatory open, it will be because everyone bought tickets to see *you*."

Even though Olivia was being nice, I felt terribly guilty.

"The observatory?" I asked. "Is it closing?"

"You didn't hear?" Olivia said. "That last storm we had did a lot of damage to the roof."

She barely took a breath in between sentences. "Remember that big leak in the ceiling? And how on rainy days a bucket had to be placed under it to catch the drips? Well, now they need lots of buckets under lots of leaks to catch the rain.

"Plus the observatory needs new computer equipment. Their computers are practically prehistoric*."

"So the festival is trying to raise enough money to keep the weather observatory open?" I asked in a weak voice.

"Yep! And if enough money is raised," Olivia answered, "we might build a science classroom." By "we" she meant all the people who volunteer at the weather observatory (including her). "It looks like *you'll* save the observatory, Layla! You're our hero!"

Some hero I am! I thought. *A half hour ago I was planning on telling Olivia I wouldn't be coming.*

I thought about the volunteers at the weather observatory who had also helped me out. There's Pam, the cashier at our local grocery store. She taught me how to play the guitar. Mr. Crane, my teacher and long-distance tutor, sends schoolwork for me to do while I'm traveling on the tour bus. My neighbor, Ms. Fruzzi, owns a clothing store and chooses what I wear for shows.

They've supported what's important to me. How could I not support something that was so important to them and our town? How could I let them down?

"Um, Layla...?" asked Olivia.

"Oh sorry," I replied. "I was just trying to think."

"About the song you wrote for the festival?" she asked. "This is so exciting. When

26

can I hear it?"

"Really soon," I said, not wanting to let on that it was not written yet.

"Alright!" she whooped. "I can't wait to see you!"

I meant it when I replied, "Me, too!"

Just like that, my decision was made to keep the Promise.

Chapter Three

RAIN TURNS INTO SUNSHINE

For the next couple of days, I tried to put thoughts about the Five Star Concert behind me, but it wasn't easy. I had doubts that I'd made the right decision.

Donna said I'd thrown the chance of a lifetime out the window.

Auntie explained the choice was "a tough nut to crack," which she says is a problem that's difficult to solve, but that I did the right thing.

My mom told me that keeping my word showed that I was loyal to the people who cared about me.

I was scheduled to be the warm-up act for a concert during the coming weekend, but the musician had a sore throat and canceled all her shows. That gave me ten days in a row off before my next performance.

We decided to head for the festival, which was a little over a week away.

The windshield wipers on the bus swished back and forth noisily. I wondered if it was raining in Majestic Mountain.

I remembered how my dad and I got caught in a rainstorm once on the mountaintop. We skedaddled* into the weather observatory until it passed by. When we stepped back outside, the most brilliant rainbow we'd ever seen arched across the sky.

I couldn't wait to see my dad, spend time with my little black-and-white Boston terrier, Jupiter, sleep in my cozy purple bedroom and hike up to the top of the mountain again.

My mom pressed the buttons on the bus radio to find a station we could hear clearly.

She stopped when she heard a news announcer's voice, "And now for your weather forecast. The report from the Majestic Mountain Weather Observatory is that it's 68 degrees and raining.

"In nearby Shaker Springs, it's 66 degrees and raining. But turn that frown upside down—our meteorologist predicts that by late afternoon, rain turns into sunshine."

"Did you hear that?" I asked my mom and Auntie. "I was just thinking about the weather observatory."

Rain turns into sunshine, I thought. *That would be a great title for a song about how even a gloomy* day can become bright.*

૮ૐ૭ ૮ૐ૭

Inside my zigzag-patterned pencil case I found my favorite pencil with the heart-shaped eraser on the end. I grabbed two little pads of bright blue and green sticky notes. I always keep them handy because ideas seem to pop up

out of nowhere.

And then came the fun part. I began composing* a song.

Thoughts started coming to me as quickly as I could scribble them on the sticky notes— "big chance," "hard choice," "afternoon showers," "rainbows and flowers" and a whole bunch more.

I stuck them on the wall and window next to me and thought about the words and ideas.

An hour or so later I had the lyrics nearly done. The song is about a girl who has a hard decision to make. A "tough nut to crack," as Auntie would say. It "rains" all over her happiness. But the choice she makes gives her a feeling as warm as sunshine.

I started plucking the strings on my guitar and putting some of the words to the tune. That's how I always think out my songs—sticky notes and strumming Old Blue, my bright blue guitar.

I played around with some chords* that

sound good together. I pressed the strings down onto the guitar neck with the fingers on my left hand and strummed across all the strings with my right hand. The rhythm* was coming along, but was not quite there yet.

Soon the bus rolled to a stop by a beautiful park. Now that the sun was out, it would be the perfect spot for lunch and the perfect place to finish writing my song.

I put Old Blue back in my polka-dotted guitar case, carried it outside and set it down on the pavement. After a morning of riding in the bus, it felt so good to bend down and touch my toes, and then stretch my arms up to the sky.

Auntie was spreading a yellow tablecloth on a picnic table beside a pond surrounded by giant willow trees.

"Layla," my mom called to me from inside the trailer. "Can you please bring these grapes and strawberries out to the picnic table?"

"Sure, Mom," I said, jumping up the stairs of the bus two at a time.

As I scooped up the bowls of fruit, I heard the loud CRA-A-A-C-K of wood splitting.

I leapt over to the bus window and saw a silver van towing a trailer with a red speedboat on it. They were parking crookedly into the spot next to us.

Something was sticking out from under one of the wheels of the trailer. It was my polka-dotted guitar case—almost completely CRUSHED!

Someone screamed. I realized it was *me*. Before I reached the bus door, the truck had pulled forward a few feet and backed into the parking space straighter. CRA-A-A-A-C-K!

Old Blue had been run over, not once, but twice!

Chapter Four

CRUSHED TO PIECES

The driver of the van apologized over and over again to us as he gathered up the crunched case and five jagged, blue pieces of the guitar from the ground. He put them on the steps of the bus and shook his head sadly.

I held the neck of the guitar in one hand. It was no longer attached to the body of the guitar. My precious Old Blue was completely ruined.

"It's my fault, not yours," I admitted to him. "I'm the one who put the guitar case down in the parking space and walked away."

"I'm still really sorry," the man said with relief. "Gee, my kids love your music. Do you think that I could get your autograph* for them?"

"Sure," I said, trying to sound cheerful. "Do you have something you'd like me to sign?"

He looked around in his van for a minute and then came out empty-handed. "I can't seem to find anything that would be good to write on."

The man glanced at the bus stairs and pointed. "Hey, how about autographing a piece of that blue guitar? Now wouldn't *that* be an interesting story for my kids?!"

Why not? I thought. *I might as well turn this bad situation into something good. Like rain turns into sunshine.*

By late afternoon on Friday we were just a few miles away from Majestic Mountain. The closer I got, the more excited I was to return home.

Mom had given me permission to use the laptop computer. I gazed* at the screen which showed a photo that Olivia had just sent to me. She and a couple of kids from the Layla Fan Club were posing by a colorful festival poster they'd taped onto the window of the local grocery store.

The poster showed a close-up picture of me singing onstage. I was playing Old Blue and wearing my glittering blue sunglasses and purple sequined vest.

I saw that Olivia had included a message with the picture: To my best friend from your best friend.

✥ ✥

Finally, the tour bus rolled into the little downtown area of Majestic Mountain. I noticed five or six people on the sidewalk, holding up big signs.

What's this? I wondered. *Is there an election*?*

As the bus came closer, I read the words on the signs:

Welcome Home, Layla!

and

Hooray for Layla!

and

We ♥ you, Layla!

The Layla Fan Club was there to greet me. My heart swelled up with such a special feeling.

Auntie pulled the tour bus over to the side of the road and we rushed outside. Olivia's face told me how thrilled she was to see me. But a couple of friends from school looked me over with surprise. I couldn't imagine why.

"Where are your fancy clothes?" my friend Beth asked. "Like your sequined vest and cool lilac sneakers."

I looked down at the jeans and plain

green shirt I was wearing.

"Why don't you have lilac color in your hair?" asked another girl named Tracy.

I tried to explain that the fancy clothes I wear onstage are just for performing and that I don't normally dress like that. "The color in my hair washes out with shampoo when the shows are over," I told them.

"Huh," Tracy said with a scowl* on her face.

"Oh," Beth said, then let out a long sigh.

"Well..." a girl named Samantha said in a hopeful voice, "can we at least see the inside of your tour bus?"

"Sure, c'mon in," I replied, hoping to do something so they weren't so disappointed.

The next day I was sitting on the back porch of my house in my favorite seat that swings back and forth. I heard the birds singing in the trees and smelled the wild mountain roses. It was a clear day and I could see all the way to Flying Fish Lake, which is at least ten miles away.

Everything was perfect for writing the new song for the festival. I had my favorite pencil and sticky notepads ready to go. It was time to let my creative ideas flow.

But...they didn't. I sat and sat and sat and sat for what seemed like hours. I had zero. Zip. Not even one idea.

To make matters worse, I had no guitar. *Of course,* I thought, *that's the reason I can't write. I'm hopeless without Old Blue.*

I was positive the guitar was the reason I'd been able to write so many songs.

As the minutes ticked by, I began to lose confidence in myself. *Maybe I'll never be able to write another good song again,* I worried.

I was looking forward to going back to my school for the week. But I was a little nervous, too. I'd been away for a long time. Would I still fit in? Would my friends include me in the games we always play during recess?

42

On Monday morning, my dad dropped me off at the entrance to the school ten minutes before the school bell rang. I had butterflies* in my stomach.

All the kids were waiting in the paved play area. The first thing I noticed was that Beth, Tracy and a few other girls were wearing glittering blue star-shaped sunglasses like the ones I was wearing in the photo on the festival poster.

It made me feel good to think that they liked my style. My butterflies started to disappear.

Sometimes it gets lonely studying in the tour bus. My mom and Auntie are there to help me learn the lessons, but it's not the same as being in a classroom.

On the other hand, I'd forgotten how loud it is at school. In the tour bus, it's quiet. I can focus. In school, even when everyone's seated, it seems like a million things are going on at once.

That morning, one kid was putting his finger inside his cheek to make popping sounds. A girl was braiding her friend's pretty red hair. Two boys were kicking a pencil back and forth across the aisle between desks like it was a soccer ball.

Another student had stashed pieces of candy in her pocket and was sneaking them one by one into her mouth. Several people were bugging her to share with them.

It all seemed more interesting than the assignment we were supposed to be doing. *I should write a song about this,* I thought.

That is what I was thinking when Mr. Crane, our teacher, passed out a surprise geography quiz. I'd learned this lesson last week while we were on the tour bus, so I was sure I'd do just fine.

Mr. Crane handed back our quizzes after we returned from art class. I was shocked* to see a whole bunch of corrections on mine, written in green pen.

Then Mr. Crane pulled a piece of paper from a tan folder on his desk. "I have some interesting news to announce," he said. "The weather observatory is holding a creative writing contest.

"If you enter, your paper can be no more than 250 words long," he read from the sheet that explained the contest rules. "It should be about how stormy weather is like stormy feelings."

He continued, "The weather observatory has made a deal with the television station that the winner will get to be the weather forecaster for a day *and* make a guest appearance on the six o'clock evening news."

The song I wrote called "Rain Turns into Sunshine" just might work for the contest, I thought. This day was shaping up better than I ever expected.

Until recess.

Chapter Five

MIXED FEELINGS

The writing contest, the writing contest, the writing contest. It's all everybody talked about at recess. Olivia was especially overjoyed.

I looked around and tried to find *somebody* who might want to play Rock Paper Scissors. I drifted over to a group of girls only to find out they were talking about the contest, too. It seemed that I was the only one who wanted to play during recess.

Sitting on the low stone wall beside the play area, I watched all the kids. They were talking excitedly and using their hands to explain their ideas.

While I was away and all I wanted to do was write and sing songs, I'd felt like an outsider*. Now that I was home and all I wanted to do was play, I *still* felt like I didn't belong.

Why is it, I thought grumpily, *that even when I'm with my friends I feel far away?*

Mr. Crane clanged the bell outside the door to let everyone know that recess was over. Kids hustled* to form a single-file line in front of him and go back into our classroom.

A joke popped into my head that I wanted to tell Olivia, but she was still busy talking about the contest. "How about this?" she asked the group. "A tornado is like jealousy. It circles around you and destroys what's in its path and..."

Enough about the contest, I fumed*. *Hmmfff!*

"...that's why," continued Olivia, "at the weather observatory—"

"Well," I blurted out in frustration, "who cares about the stupid contest? And what's so important about the weather observatory, anyway?"

Olivia stopped talking for the first time in about 15 minutes. She tilted her head to the side and looked at me. There was no expression on her face, though. I couldn't tell what she was thinking.

Out of the corner of my eye, I saw Mr. Crane frowning at me.

He quickly called out, "Time to go in, class!"

During study time, Mr. Crane motioned for me to come up to his desk. I figured that he probably wanted to ask me if I would autograph my photo or something like that.

"Layla," Mr. Crane said, "you are a good student. I know that you could have done better on the quiz."

This was not what I expected him to say. I stumbled over my words. "Ahh, um, I think so, too."

"I'll tell you what," he said. "I know it's tough getting back into the swing of being in school. Do you want to do a project for extra credit?"

"What's extra credit?" I asked.

"It's a project that you can do in addition to your regular homework and it will help raise your grade," he replied.

"Oh yes, please," I said, nodding my head.

"Good then," Mr. Crane said, as he handed me a folded piece of paper. "Here is your assignment. It's due this Friday."

I thanked him and returned to my seat. The paper read:

Layla's Extra-Credit Project:

What Is a Weather Observatory and

Why Is It Important?

1. Visit the weather observatory, read about it and talk to someone who works there.
2. Give a 5-minute speech to the class on Friday at 11:30 a.m. that answers the question above.

Five minutes?! I thought. *How can I talk about a weather observatory for five whole minutes? It's a crumbling, leaky, old building at the top of a mountain!*

BOR-ING! In my mind I imagined myself giving the talk to a class that was yawning, looking out the window and doodling.

❧ ❧

The next day, recess was a whole lot more

fun. We played Capture the Kadoodle, which is almost the same as tag. It was a blast and just like old times.

Mr. Crane clanged the bell and we all rushed to line up in front of him. As we waited for one of the kids to run back and get his sweatshirt, Olivia made an announcement.

"Attention, everyone! This weekend is the Majestic Fest!" she exclaimed. "Bring your brothers, sisters, parents, grandparents, cousins, aunts, uncles, neighbors, friends, and anyone and everyone to hear Layla!

"She's written what is a soon-to-be-a-hit song!" Olivia said proudly.

I felt so embarrassed and guilty. Somehow, it felt like I was part of a lie.

"Will you sing it for us, Layla?" one of my classmates asked me.

"Yeah! Will you?" asked another.

"C'mon!" a few people said at once. "Sing it! Sing it!"

"Nope," I said. "It's a surprise."

Little did they know what a big surprise it would be—to them and to me! The festival was four days away and I hadn't even *started* the song yet.

That afternoon, my dad and I took Jupiter for a walk up the mountain to take pictures of where the observatory's science room might be built. I was planning on putting the photos on the poster board I was making to go along with my speech.

I'd walked that route a gazillion times. It made me remember how much I'd enjoyed the Lunch-and-Learn Labs at the weather observatory. On the first Monday of the month, my whole class would hike up to the observatory, have a picnic lunch and then do fun weather-related experiments.

We investigated how sunscreens work, figured out ways to make wind power and learned weather safety for every season.

I began to relax more and more as my feet traveled the steep, rocky path. The fragrance of pink wild roses filled the air. Mmmmm...they smelled as beautiful as they looked.

"Dad," I said, "I have a problem."

"What's up?" he asked.

"I know you're working on borrowing a guitar for me to play until we can find a new one," I told him. "Here's the thing, Dad. I'm having a tough time writing the song for the festival. Without Old Blue, I just can't seem to find the words or music."

My dad shook his head. "The truth is, Layla, music comes *through* your guitar, but it comes *from* your heart."

"But Dad," I whined, "don't you think it's a little strange that as soon as Old Blue was crushed, so was my confidence for making music?"

"Talent is a gift that comes from within you," my dad said. "And one that you make better by practice.

"Sure, there are some days when nothing sounds right," he continued. "But then a moment comes along where you have so many ideas, you can't write the words down fast enough. Trust me on this one."

I wanted to, but I was not completely convinced.

Chapter Six

TIME'S RUNNING OUT

Even though Majestic Mountain is huge, the town that's named after the mountain is fairly small. So it wasn't too surprising that my dad and I ran into Beth and Tracy at the top of the mountain.

When my dad went to toss his empty water bottle into the recycling bin, Beth and Tracy half whispered to me that they agreed with what I'd said in class about the weather observatory.

"What's the big fuss about this weather observatory?" Tracy asked.

"Yeah, who cares?" said Beth. "Look at it. It's like a hundred thousand million years old or something."

"There's not even a soda machine here,"

Tracy added.

Something dawned* on me. My choices—good and not so good—can change how other people think and act. I'd complained about the weather observatory and now other people were, too.

My star-shaped glasses, my hair, my bad attitude...like it or not, people want to follow what I do. I had a responsibility to make better choices.

❧ ❧

On our way home from school the next day, my mom and I spotted a yellow poster board that was tacked to a tree:

YARD SALE TODAY!
Good stuff cheap!

My mom never ever passes by a yard sale. She pulled the car over and headed straight for a table covered in paperback books.

The yard sale was huge. It looked like the people who lived there moved everything that was in the house out of the house. Stuff was piled high on tables, covered the grass and was spread out on blankets.

My eyes scanned the furniture and vases and baskets and toys and then—WHOA!—something very interesting leaning up against a gigantic oak tree. I hurried over to check out a

tall, curvy, flowered guitar case.

I wanted to open it right away, but at the same time I didn't. What if there was a beautiful guitar inside? That would be fantastic. But what if it was empty?

There was only one way to find out. I put my hand on the case and unsnapped the rusty silver latch on the cover. I slowly opened the lid.

What was inside wasn't exactly beautiful, but it was an old guitar. Long scratches marked the front. One of the strings was broken and dangling. As I turned it over, a pink guitar pick with an orange bird on it dropped out of the sound hole in the center of the guitar.

Without thinking, I used the pick to strum a few chords. I was surprised to discover that even with the broken string, the guitar sounded pretty good. I knew that the broken string would be easy to replace.

After turning the tuning pegs that stick out from the head of the guitar to tune the strings, I strummed a few more chords.

The sound from the beat-up old guitar was clear and beautiful. I can't describe why exactly, but the guitar felt just right in my hands.

"So you like to play?" a smiling woman with short silvery hair asked me.

I guessed that she didn't recognize me. "Yes, I do," I said. "Very much."

"I can tell by the way you played that melody," she said. "You're good, too."

"Thank you," I replied.

"I haven't picked up that guitar in years, but oh, the fun I used to have playing it!" Her smile was bright as she recalled the memory. "I'd be thrilled if you fixed it up and let it make music again."

The old woman pulled a rag out of her pocket and began dusting the guitar off. "It could use a coat of paint, I think." She leaned the guitar against the tree, backed away from it and looked it over, up and down. "Pink."

"Pink?" I asked, trying to imagine a pink guitar. I wasn't so sure about that. "Or maybe blue," I suggested, thinking about Old Blue.

"Definitely pink," she said. "Absolutely pink." Then she put the guitar in the case, closed the latch and handed the guitar case to me.

"OK," I said. "How much would you like to sell it for?"

"Sell it?!" she said with a snort. "I just want to hear your song."

I wasn't sure what she meant. "My song?"

"The song you wrote for the festival," she said with a smile. "Help keep the observatory open. That's all the payment I need."

So she *did* recognize me. I looked into her pretty green eyes. Something seemed familiar about her, too.

As my mom and I walked to the car—her with an armful of books and me with my "new" old guitar, my mom whispered, "I can't believe Pinkie McCue gave you her guitar!"

I gasped. I'd just talked to the most famous female musician ever to come from our state!

✦ ✦

Crouching down in my backyard, I dipped a paintbrush into the can of paint that my mom and I had just bought at the hardware store. I smiled and shook my head. *Am I actually going*

to paint this guitar bright pink?

"Hey there!" Olivia shouted. She was fumbling to get through the fence gate with two big bags, so I scrambled over to help her.

"Check this out," Olivia said as she unrolled a whole bunch of the festival posters with my photo on them.

"I'm on my way to my uncle's birthday party soon, but I wondered if you wanted to help me add glitter around the borders of the posters to make them really stand out," Olivia said. "Oh, I see you're in the middle of a project."

Olivia raised her eyebrows. "Pink, huh? Very bold, Layla. I like it!"

"It wasn't my idea, but I think I'll like it, too," I said.

"You keep painting that and I'll sprinkle glitter on these," Olivia said. She spread the posters out on the grass, along with white glue and a jar of pink glitter. "Just think! The Majestic Fest is in three days!"

Hearing her say that made me panic*. *Time's running out,* I thought. *Will I be able to start—let alone finish—the song in time?*

Even though I felt frustrated and anxious, I tried hard to hide my feelings as we talked about the writing contest. Olivia was still bubbling over with ideas.

When the guitar was done, I stood back to admire it. "What do you think?" I asked.

She squinted and pointed. "You missed one little spot right there. Here, I'll show you."

As she jumped up, she stumbled and the glitter went flying—across the wet paint on my pink guitar!

Chapter Seven

WILD ROSE

Olivia stared at the guitar, put her hands over her open mouth and sucked in a big gulp of air.

I stared at Olivia and exploded, "Look what you've done! Why do you have to keep sticking your nose in everything?!"

"I'm so sorry, Layla!" Olivia cried.

My fists were clenched at my sides. I didn't dare speak.

"Say something, Layla," Olivia said.

I don't really think I was angry at her as much as I was frustrated about so many things:

#1 Turning down the big concert (ugh!)

#2 Hearing Old Blue being crushed (ouch!)

#3 Working on an extra-credit project (*stress*ful!)

#4 Having a tough time writing a song for the Majestic Fest (yikes!)

#5 And last but not least, seeing my pink guitar messed up with glitter (grrrr!)

"Fine then!" Olivia's voice was shaky, like she was about to cry. "If that's how you're going to be, I'm going!" She grabbed all the posters, rolled them up and stomped through the fence gate.

The glitter, which had sprayed across about half of the guitar, was stuck in the paint. I groaned and tried to pick it out of the paint. It was useless.

What a mess, I thought, as I sat with my head in my hands and legs crisscross-applesauce on the grass. *At least the glitter covers the scratches.*

When I looked up, my guitar was sparkling in the sunlight. It actually looked pretty.

The glitter jar was lying on its side in the grass. It gave me an idea. I sprinkled glitter on the rest of the guitar.

Gorgeous! I thought. *It reminds me of the color of the fragrant pink roses that grow wild on Majestic Mountain. Wild Rose. I'll name this guitar Wild Rose.*

I knew that I should call Olivia and tell her I understood that accidents happen and apologize for yelling. But by then she was already on the way to her uncle's birthday party. I'd have to wait.

To put the fight out of my mind, I decided to give the festival song another try by writing some words on sticky notes. I didn't have any ideas, so I just jotted down the first words that came into my mind: "broccoli," "tree fort," "shoelaces" and "rhinoceros."

You're going to write a song about a rhinoceros and shoelaces? I asked myself. *Not good!*

The harder I thought, the more I paced around the room. Back and forth and back and forth from my bed to my closet.

I hummed a little, trying out a melody. Nothing sounded right. The new paint on Wild Rose was still drying, so I couldn't string together any chords.

Flopping onto my bed, I yelped "Help!" into my pillow.

I decided to work on my extra-credit project instead. I asked my mom if she'd help me to do a search on the computer about the weather observatory.

After we printed out a whole bunch of articles, I stretched out on the comfy little couch in my room and began reading about the history of the observatory's tower.

I was surprised to learn that the observatory has been keeping track of wind speed, wind direction and temperature for over a hundred years.

Why is it so important to know what the temperature was in 1920, 1947, 1999 or any year? I wondered. I kept reading and found the answer. Scientists compare measurements over time and study trends*. Most climate* scientists using weather observatory measurements and other information think that the planet is heating up faster than ever before—this is called global warming.

Global warming could cause flooding, affect farming and threaten animal survival, including polar bears.

Another article I read talked about the weather observatory's study on pollution and how it might someday kill all the wild mountain roses.

What?! That sure got my attention. I couldn't imagine the mountain without roses.

I was surprised when my mom poked her head inside my bedroom doorway and said it was time to get ready for bed.

Already? It was too late to call Olivia. How had an hour and a half flown by so quickly?

Chapter Eight

APOLOGY ACCEPTED

The next morning when I woke up, I sensed that something was wrong. I opened my eyes and looked around my room. Everything seemed fine.

I let my eyelids flutter shut as I wondered what this strange feeling was all about. Aha! A familiar smell was missing—coffee brewing. My mom makes a pot every morning.

"We'll have to stop at Peach's Pie and Coffee Shop for my cup of joe*," my mom said as I poured milk into a bowl of cereal for breakfast. "The coffeemaker is acting wacky."

I soon found out that wasn't the only thing that was acting wacky. When I looked in the mirror, I saw that my hair was, too.

It was a very muggy* morning and my hair was doing what I call "The Boing!" Frizz city! I had to put on a hat to get it to behave.

The waiting line at the coffee shop snaked in a big "U" shape. The woman at the front of the line was having a hard time deciding if she should buy a blueberry or apple or banana cream pie.

Craning my neck, I counted how many people were ahead of us...one, two, three, four, five, six, seven. I worried that I wouldn't get to school early. There was something important I needed to do before class started.

I felt terrible that I'd shouted at my best friend. I wasn't mad at Olivia. I was frustrated with myself and it was time to tell her.

The truth is, Olivia has always been there for me. Always happy for my successes. Always telling anyone who would listen that I can rock a song like nobody else.

I pulled a teeny-tiny, folded piece of paper out of my backpack. It was a greeting card that I'd made which was about the size of my thumb. On the front was a smiley face in a heart. Inside it said in itty-bitty writing:

The world's smallest card
for a great big apology.
I'm sorry, Olivia.
XOXOXO,
Layla

The woman behind us tapped me on the shoulder. It was Ms. Brill, the Program Director for the weather observatory. "Layla," Ms. Brill said, "I hardly recognized you with your hair in a ponytail and your hat on."

"It's a bad hair day," I admitted with a laugh. "It's nice to see you, Ms. Brill."

"I have just the thing for you," she told me. "I think you'd like the Frizz Fun class at the observatory this afternoon from 3:00 to 3:30. It's all about humidity."

"What's humidity?" I asked.

"You'll have to come to the class to find out," she said with a wink. "And right before that, there's a Wind-Watching and Cloud-Spotting Workshop."

"That sounds interesting," I agreed.

She and my mother chatted for another minute or so.

Ms. Brill turned to me. "Your mother tells me that you're doing a presentation about the weather observatory."

While we slowly inched forward in line, Ms. Brill told me about measuring humidity with a hair hygrothermograph.

"A hair hygro*what*?" I asked.

She laughed. "A hair hygrothermograph uses strands of human hair to measure and record the humidity on a chart. It also has a temperature sensor which writes on a separate part of the same chart."

"It uses a real hair?" I wondered.

"Yes, it's a real hair," Ms. Brill said,

nodding her head.

I tried to imagine what a machine that was made with a hair might look like. *I have to see this*, I thought.

"Next!" the cashier hollered from behind the counter. "May I please help who's next?"

"Oh! That's us," my mom said with a wave goodbye to Ms. Brill. "We'll see you this afternoon."

When my mom pulled the car up in front of my school, it was 7:58 a.m. Two minutes until the bell rang for the beginning of class!

I ran up the front steps, flung open the door and dashed across the hall into my classroom. Scurrying down the third row at superhero speed, I slipped the world's smallest card onto Olivia's desk and plunked myself onto my seat.

Whew! I'd made it before the bell rang.

I looked up to the whiteboard where Mr. Crane was writing "Good Morning" with a blue marker. My eyes stopped when I saw Olivia looking back at me. She was grinning from ear to ear and pointing to a big, round button pin she was wearing.

Olivia had drawn blue star-shaped glasses on the button. Above them she'd written: "Majestic Fest Countdown" and below them: "2 days away!"

Chapter Nine

WIND WATCHING

"You might think it's pretty silly to say you can watch the wind," Ms. Brill told the 16 kids and adults in the Wind-Watching and Cloud-Spotting Workshop. "Raise your hand if you think air is invisible."

I raised my hand and noticed that Olivia didn't raise hers. She'd signed up for the workshop, too, so we were sitting next to each other.

Ms. Brill smiled. "Let's see. Seven people think it is and nine people think it's not. The answer is that we can't see air, even though it's all around us. But wind is air that's in motion, so we can see what it does."

She continued, "How have you 'seen' wind?"

People in the class shouted out answers.

"Wind makes a kite fly."

"It moves sailboats across the water."

"Wind makes trees sway."

"It piles up snowdrifts in my yard that make great snow forts!"

Later, we went outside and talked about clouds and how they are made of tiny water droplets or ice crystals.

Ms. Brill explained that clouds can help predict if good weather or bad weather is on the way.

"Did you know," she asked us, "that even though clouds look light and fluffy, many weigh as much as an airplane?"

"Wow!" a few people murmured.

"Look!" I shouted, pointing to a cloud above a mountain in the distance. "That cloud looks like a flying saucer!"

"That is called a lenticular altocumulus cloud," Ms. Brill told our class.

Olivia and I stayed for the Frizz Fun class,

which explained that humidity is water vapor that's in the air—and it's what can sometimes make my hair look like springs sticking out of my head!

Ms. Brill explained that hair hygrometers, which tell the humidity and use long strands of hair, have been used by weather stations for over 200 years because they work so well to measure humidity.

Remembering what Ms. Brill had talked about at the coffee shop, I raised my hand. "What's the difference between a hygrometer and a hygrothermograph?"

"Great question, Layla," Ms. Brill said. "A hygrometer measures humidity. A hygrothermograph measures humidity *and* temperature and records them on a chart."

Olivia and I learned how to make our own simple hair hygrometers using a long piece of my hair as a string, a milk carton, a penny, a toothpick and a few other craft supplies.

After the classes, I had a new problem— too much information for my extra-credit project! How could I ever cram it all into a five-minute speech?

Chapter Ten

THE BEST DAY EVER

On Friday, the day before the Majestic Fest, I woke up at 5:07 a.m. (which is way too early for me!). Right away I noticed the smell of freshly brewed coffee.

When I stumbled sleepily into the kitchen, my mom was patting the coffeemaker and looking very proud that she'd figured out how to fix it.

"Good morning, Layla," she said brightly. "You're up early."

She put a plate in front of me with whole-wheat toast smothered in delicious blueberry jam. Then she poured orange juice into a green mug printed with the advice:

**Make today
the best day ever.**

After I gobbled up my breakfast, I knew just what to do to make that happen.

I brushed my teeth, put on my sparkly pink guitar-shaped earrings and carried my guitar case out to the back porch. Happily, I settled onto the porch swing and Jupiter joined me. I opened the lid of the case. My new pink guitar sparkled and shined as if to say it was ready to be played.

Big, white, puffy clouds drifted across the brilliant blue sky. I knew from my Wind-Watching and Cloud-Spotting Workshop that these are called cumulus clouds. A gentle breeze carried the scent of the wild flowers to me.

My fingers automatically strummed the strings of Wild Rose and the rich notes vibrated into the air.

Without thinking, I began humming and writing words on my bright blue, yellow and green sticky notes: "mountain air" and "blue skies," "birdsongs," "sun," "wild roses," "memories" and "family."

82

These words got me started in the right direction. Then everything came together—the ideas, the lyrics, the melody—inspired* by my feelings for the town I've grown up in and the friendships I've made there.

I guess Dad was right, I thought. Being able to write songs had nothing to do with the guitar—it *was* inside me the whole time.

I was on a roll*. There was one more thing I could do to make this the best day ever. Practice my speech about the weather observatory—one final time.

The first time I practiced out loud and timed it on my clock, it was 16 minutes long. Finally, I got it down to five minutes (but I had to talk really really really fast!). Mission* accomplished!

    ❧ ❧

At 11:32 that morning, I was speed-talking in the front of the classroom. I saw a hand raised in the very back row of the class.

"Yes, Mr. Crane," I said. "Do you have a question?"

"Your extra-credit project is so interesting, Layla," he said. "We don't want to miss a single thing. I suggest slowing down a little so we can hear what you're saying. There's plenty of time. No need to rush."

Taking his advice, I slowed way down.

Nobody had yawned, looked out the window or doodled. Everyone seemed to want to hear about the weather observatory.

I asked Mr. Crane if I could use three more minutes and he gave me a thumb's up. I lifted Wild Rose from where I'd hidden the guitar case behind Mr. Crane's desk.

"Here's that surprise I told you about a few days ago," I said to the class. "No one has heard this song I wrote for the festival yet. I'd like to know what you think before I play it tomorrow."

When I started the first few notes, the class became completely silent. And when I finished, everyone whooped and hoorayed. They loved it!

✿ ✿

That afternoon after school, I met Olivia at the observatory.

Suddenly, huge dark gray clouds swept across the sky. Thunder boomed, lightning lit up the valley and rain came pounding down on the observatory roof. Drips began freckling the floor.

A couple of people who work at the observatory rushed into action and grabbed rags, mops and large buckets out of the storage room.

Olivia and I darted here and there, putting buckets under the leaks and furiously mopping up water with the rags so no one would slip.

"I see what you mean about the roof," I told Olivia.

"We're in for a nasty storm," I heard a visitor in a red-and-white striped tee shirt say to his friend who was wearing a purple baseball cap.

"It's going to be a whopper," Mr. Purple Baseball Cap replied.

Oh no! I worried. *Volunteers are supposed to set up for the Majestic Fest tonight, and all the events start early tomorrow morning.*

If the Majestic Fest is canceled, I wondered,

what will happen to the weather observatory?

Money for the tickets would need to be returned to the people who bought them. That would mean no money to fix the leaky roof or to build a science room.

I fretted* as I walked back and forth from the window to the buckets to the window. I hoped for a sign that the dark clouds were clearing.

"It's supposed to last all weekend," Mr. Striped Tee Shirt said to his friend.

Chapter Eleven

LAYLA ROCKS!

Olivia put her hands lightly on my shoulders and steered me into a chair. "Take a deep breath, Layla," she advised. "You're wearing down a path in this poor carpet with all that pacing."

"Why are you so calm?" I asked Olivia. "This could ruin the Majestic Fest!"

"Not going to happen," Olivia said confidently. "The show will go on."

I wanted to believe it was true. "How can you be so sure? Do you have a crystal ball? That guy in the striped tee shirt said—"

Olivia laughed. "No, silly, I don't need a crystal ball. And that guy isn't a weather geek like me. All these computers and weather tools might be old and need to be updated* but they can still help predict the weather. Come on over here."

Olivia pointed to the computer screen, which showed the storm was slowly heading east and away from Majestic Mountain.

"The way it looks right now, the rain should stop later tonight," Ms. Brill added.

At that moment I couldn't have been happier to have a "weather geek" for a best friend.

I thought the day before had been the best day ever, but the next morning was promising to be even better.

For starters, the sunlight was streaming in my window when I woke up. I knew that the festival was on!

Then the phone rang, and it was one of the Brisbee brothers—calling to talk to *me*! He told me that they really admired what I was doing to help the community and they were going to make a donation* to the observatory. He also said they'd still like me to be the warm-up act for them sometime.

Best of all, the turnout at the Majestic Fest was bigger than anyone expected. Hundreds of people came by bicycles, cars, skateboards and their own two feet.

Everyone was in good spirits, ready to enjoy all the activities and support the weather observatory.

My favorite event was the tagged balloon launches. Tagged balloons are small helium balloons, about as tall as a piece of notebook paper. Each has a tag that's printed with the observatory's phone number and email address and the person's name who releases it to float up into the sky.

The tag asks the person who finds the balloon to call or email the Majestic Mountain Weather Observatory so they can keep track of how far the balloon travels.

About one in ten balloons are actually

found. Some balloons travel over a hundred miles!

I wondered how far mine would float and who would find it.

I was more excited than nervous getting ready to perform. I wore my blue star-shaped sunglasses, striped shirt and sequined vest. My hair had touches of washable lilac color. And I put on my favorite lilac sneakers.

As the announcer came out onstage and greeted the audience, I took a deep breath and peeked from behind a big sound speaker.

About five hundred people were standing and sitting in lawn chairs or on blankets they'd spread on the grass. Some people had arrived at five o'clock in the morning (when it was still a little dark!) to get seats close to the stage.

The Layla Fan Club was right up front in the first row.

I put the pink-and-black guitar strap of

Wild Rose over my shoulder and got set to run onto the stage as soon as the announcer introduced me. As I waited, I looked up into the blue sky just in time to see to see a ginormous* puffy white cloud, in the shape of a heart, floating overhead.

"Here she is folks, the musician you've been waiting for! Our very own LAYLA!" the announcer boomed into the microphone before handing it over to me.

"Hello, Majestic Mountain!" I shouted. "There's no place I'd rather be. THANK YOU!"

The crowd cheered wildly and fans held up signs with my name on them. Two girls had written in purple marker on a huge white bed sheet in gigantic letters:

Layla Rocks!!!

"Seeing all of you coming out today to support our observatory—well, the best way I know to tell you how I feel about our mountain and the people who live here is to sing about it," I said, playing a few notes.

There were a few loud whistles and shouts, and then a hush came over the crowd.

"Here's a song that I wrote especially for the festival. It's called *Right Here with You*."

Let me tell you from the start,
this song is from my heart.
I'll sing it clear and loud,
Majestic Mountain makes me proud.

Chorus*:
There's no luckier girl in the world.
Than me. Right here. With you.

Wind tickling the trees,
fragrant whispers in the breeze,
birdsongs fill the air,
nature's beauty everywhere.

There's no luckier girl in the world.
Than me. Right here. With you.

All the faces that I see
show love for our community
by gathering here together
to support the science of weather.

*There's no luckier girl in the world.
Than me. Right here. With you.*

A beautiful mountain view,
friendships that are true.
No matter how far I roam,
these memories bring me home.

*There's no luckier girl in the world.
Than me. Right here. With you.
Right here. With you…*

The applause was thunderous*. I sang and played six more songs and asked the Layla Fan Club to come up onstage and sing the last number* with me.

That turned out to be a lot of fun. They got the crowd clapping all together in rhythm with the music.

After the last song, Olivia presented to me a bouquet of pink wild roses she'd picked from her yard.

I stuck my nose into the flowers and took a big whiff. Simply…majestic!

Chapter Twelve

ON THE AIR

A few months later, I was back in Majestic Mountain, but Olivia wasn't.

She was in a nearby town at a television station, filming her guest appearance as weather forecaster for the day. (Yes, she won the writing contest with one of her many fantastic ideas!)

"And now, folks," Olivia said in her professional newscaster's voice, "an interview with Layla, who speaks to us live* from the Majestic Mountain Weather Observatory. Layla, can you tell us about the new improvements there at the observatory?"

"Yes, it's very exciting here, Olivia," I said, looking directly at the camera that was set up inside the weather observatory.

"Construction started on the science room

last week, so more kids and adults will be able to take classes and workshops. And the observatory is planning a summer camp about weather and nature."

"What else can you show us?" Olivia asked.

"The roof was replaced and walls that were damaged by the storms were fixed."

I pointed to a wall lined with computers. "These were also purchased with the money that the festival raised. They help show weather patterns and predict storms.

"As you can see out this window, there are more picnic tables, too.

"Also, the weather observatory is pet-friendly. There is a shady area with a water faucet that's especially for filling dog bowls. And the new snack bar isn't just for people, it sells dog snacks, too."

"Thanks for the tour, Layla. Stay tuned, viewers," Olivia said, "we'll be back right after a quick commercial break."

A few minutes later, Olivia was back on the air. "OK, we're back and I wanted to remind

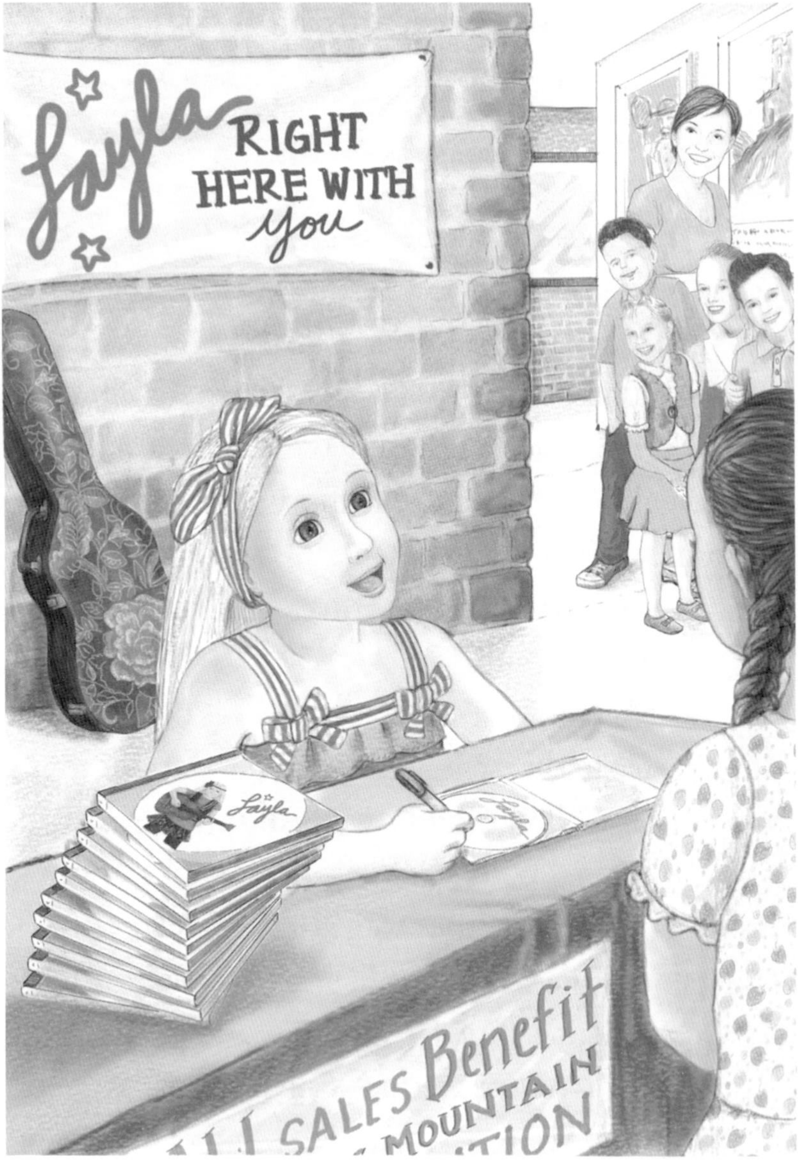
Layla
RIGHT HERE WITH you
Layla
SALES Benefit
MOUNTAIN

everyone to stop by the weather observatory today.

"Layla is there until five o'clock tonight, autographing her new CD named after the hit song, *Right Here with You*. All the money from sales of the CD today goes to the weather observatory."

It was true. My first CD had just hit the stores!

Some music industry bigwigs* had been in the audience the day of the festival and heard me perform the song I wrote. I guess they really liked it, because the next week Donna called me to say I had an offer to create a CD of my original songs.

But even before that, as my mom, Auntie and I were heading out of town in the tour bus a few hours after the festival, I was sure of one thing: when I do my very best, happiness will come whether or not I follow the trail to fame*.

When I'd said I would keep my promise to friends and family, I thought I was missing out on something big. Instead I gained something bigger. People I missed. A place I love. A song from my heart.

Glossary

Many words have more than one meaning. Here are the definitions of words marked with this symbol * (an asterisk) as they are used in sentences.

annoyed: *irritated*

annually: *happening once every year*

autograph: *hand-written name signed by a famous person*

bigwigs: *people who have important jobs*

break: *chance*

butterflies, as in "butterflies in my stomach": *a nervous feeling*

celebrity: *an important person who is well-known*

chords: *three or more notes played at the same time*

chorus: *a part of a song that is repeated after the verses*

climate: *weather in an area*

composing: *writing*

dawned, as in "dawned on me": *became understood*

demonstration: *showing how something is done*

donation: *money that is given for a good cause or charity*

election: *a process of voting for a person for a government job*

entertain: *keep things fun and interesting*

fame: *being known by many people*

festival: *celebration*

fretted: *worried*

fumed: *thought angrily*

gazed: *looked thoughtfully*

ginormous: *enormous*

gloomy: *dark and without cheer*

hustled: *hurried*

inspired: *caused a creative thought or action*

joe, as in "cup of joe": *coffee*

kitchenette: *small kitchen*

live: *a performance or interview shown as it is happening (not pre-recorded)*

lyrics: *the words of a song*

meteorologist: *a weather forecaster or scientist who studies the weather*

mission: *an important goal*
motored: *traveled or drove*
muggy: *warm and humid (water vapor
    in the air)*
number: *song*
original: *the only one of its kind*
outsider: *a person who does not belong
    to a group*
panic: *feel fear*
prehistoric: *very old*
rhythm: *sounds that are repeated*
roll, as in "on a roll": *having success*
scowl: *an irritated look*
shocked: *surprised*
skedaddled: *hurried*
thunderous: *loud*
trends: *the way something (such as weather)
    may be changing over time*
updated: *made with the latest information*
vibrating: *moving back and forth quickly*

Power of a Girl Initiative

For every Our Generation doll, outfit or accessory you buy, a portion of sales goes to Free The Children's Power of a Girl Initiative to help provide girls in developing countries an education—the most powerful tool in the world for escaping poverty.

Did you know that out of the millions of children who aren't in school, 70% of them are girls? In developing communities around the world, many girls can't go to school. Usually it's because there's no school available or because their responsibilities to family (farming, earning an income, walking hours each day for water) prevent it.

Free The Children has now built more than 650 schools which educate more than 55,000 children throughout the developing world. Free The Children also builds and fosters sustainable villages through healthcare, water programs and alternate income projects for moms and dads that give girls the opportunity to get the education they need.

The most incredible part is that most of Free The Children's funding comes from kids just like you, holding lemonade stands, bake sales, penny drives, walkathons and more.

Just by buying an Our Generation doll or accessory you have helped change the world, and you are powerful (beyond belief!) to help even more.

If you want to find out more, visit:
www.ogdolls.com/free-the-children

FREE THE CHILDREN
children helping children through education

Free The Children provided the factual information pertaining to their organization.
Free The Children is a 501c3 organization.

Write Your Own (Silly) Story

Layla's friend, Olivia, loves everything weather-related. You can be like her and show your creative side, too. Make a few copies of this story. Next, fill in the blanks with adjectives, verbs, adverbs, nouns and exclamations. You can choose from the list on page 105 or come up with your own words. Now read your story—hilarious! Put a whole new twist on the story every time you use different words.

Dear Weather Forecaster,

I'm writing to let you know that I invented a tool that predicts the weather! It's a (adjective) _____ (noun) _____ that's over (number) _____ feet long and (adjective) _____. (Exclamation) _____! This week, it was (verb) _____ up and down and pointing to a fluffy (color) _____ cumulus cloud that looked like a (noun) _____. Within minutes, it began (adverb) _____ raining (same noun as the one used in the sentence before this) _____. You don't see that every day! One morning last summer, my invention used a (noun) _____ to (adverb) _____ draw a snowman with a (adjective) _____ (noun) _____ on the (adjective) _____ wall. (Exclamation) _____! That made my mother start (verb) _____. She didn't like it at all. And then she looked out the window.

"There must be (number) _____ feet of snow

on the ground!" my mother said (adverb) _____.

See what I mean? This (adjective) _____ invention really works! You'll want to see it with your own eyes. Please call me and I'll have my (noun) _____ bring it to you at the television station.

With great pride,

Inventor (your name here) _____

Adjectives
(describe a thing or person)
chilly
delicious
dizzy
fuzzy
ginormous
grumpy
hairy
hungry
prickly
rotten
salty
slippery
sour
sparkly
squishy
striped
wrinkled

Verbs (action words)
frowning
giggling
hiccupping
hooting
humming
jumping
skipping
sneezing
stomping
wiggling

Number or Color
(you pick!)

Adverbs
(tell how something happens)
amazingly
awfully
boldly
calmly
crazily
gladly
mysteriously
noisily
politely
quickly
quietly
sleepily
surprisingly

Nouns
(persons, places or things)
cupcake
ghost
jellyfish
marshmallow
pickle
pizza
scarecrow
toenail
whistle
zebra

Exclamations
(show excitement)
Awesome!
Fantabulous!
Fiddlesticks!
Hot-diggity-dog!
Kaboom!
Oopsy-daisy!
Shazam!
Whoa!
Wow!
Yikes!

this is our story

We are an extraordinary generation of girls. And have we got a story to tell.

Our Generation is unlike any that has come before. We're helping our families learn to recycle, holding bake sales to support charities, and holding penny drives to build homes for orphaned children in Haiti. We're helping our little sisters learn to read and even making sure the new kid at school has a place to sit in the cafeteria.

All that and we still find time to play hopscotch and hockey. To climb trees, do cartwheels all the way down the block and laugh with our friends until milk comes out of our noses. You know, to be kids.

Will we have a big impact on the world? We already have. What's ahead for us? What's ahead for the world? We have no idea. We're too busy grabbing and holding on to the joy that is today.

Yep. This is our time. This is our story.

www.ogdolls.com

About the Author

Susan Cappadonia Love lives in Milton, Massachusetts with her husband, Scott (who provided the imagination for many of the ideas in this story) and daughters, Sophie and Olivia. They've hiked up Great Blue Hill—which is the highest peak on the east coast from Boston to Miami—at least a hundred times together.

While the weather observatory in this book is fictional, the Blue Hill Observatory is real and inspired the theme of the story. A big thank you to Don McCasland at the Blue Hill Observatory in Milton, Massachusetts for lending his expertise and generously sharing his knowledge about weather and climate.

This story also came to life because of all the wonderful people who contributed their creativity and vision, including Joe Battat, Dany Battat, Batia Tarrab, Jenny Gambino, Natalie Cohen, Loredana Ramacieri, Karen Erlichman, Sandy Jacinto, Véronique Casavant, Véronique Chartrand, Lisa Armstrong, Joanne Burke Casey and Pam Shrimpton.

In addition to **A Song from My Heart,** Susan has also written nine other books in the Our Generation® Series: **The Circus and the Secret Code, Magic Under the Stars, The Most Fantabulous Pajama Party Ever, The Jukebox Babysitters, The Dress in the Window, The Sweet Shoppe Mystery, The Mystery of the Vanishing Coin, Stars in Your Eyes** and **One Smart Cookie,** as well as other children's books.